Shade

of A

For Robin
Lovely to meet you!

T A Kimpton

DISCORD COMICS

Shades of A
Published by Khaos as part of Discord Comics

This is a work of parody. It imitates an author's style and work for comic and educational effect. The dialogue, names and actions of the characters are all fictional and any similarities to other works are included only to enhance the overall value of the parody. Any resemblance to actual persons, living or dead, is a coincidence.

All material contained herein is ©2014 Tab Kimpton. All rights reserved. Shades of A contains materials originally published online at http://www.DiscordComics.com as Shades of A pages 1-124 ©2013-2014.

No portion of this publication may be reproduced or transmitted unless by express permission of the author, except for the purposes of review.

References

E L James (2012). *Fifty Shades of Grey*. London: Arrow Books. p1-p514.

Stephenie Meyer (2006) *Twilight*. London: Atom p1-p498

Printed in the UK

First printing July 2014

ISBN 978-0-9570403-5-9

Preface

Shades of A began as a stupid little joke about writing a queer version of the infamous Fifty Shades of Grey, and spiralled from there. I borrowed a copy of the book, and crawled through it, annotating as I went, starting with witty little comments but soon spiralling down into 'oh god why' and 'Arrrg stop!' the angrier I got.

See, I've been an on/off member of the kink community for years and met some of the nicest sets of people I've had the pleasure to chat to, and here was a book telling the world that being a creepy rapist in an unhealthy, controlling relationship is how being a dom works.

But getting angry wouldn't change anything, so instead I sat down and wrote something. I wanted a story that showed the social side of kink- the friendship with people that have kinks that you've never even heard of, the geeky side hobbies everyone has and the thick rope of black humour knotting it all together.

From that Chris Slate was born. Most men I've met with high powered, high stress jobs are submissive- the theory being that they have to take control all the time, so what's more relieving and fun but to let someone else make the decisions for a change?

I sometimes feel like I'm on a mission to write minority characters and get some representation out there. This is partly why I write what I do, but also out of a desire to challenge myself, get out of my comfort zones and challenge the reader too. So in an setting steeped in hyper-sexuality, I chose to make the main character, and love interest, an asexual muslim with a chip on his shoulder.

I put out an announcement that I was after personal stories from people who identified or had knowledge of being Genderqueer, Asexual, Thai, Muslim or Pakistani. I got slews and slews of emails, proving that once again, here was a bunch of people that never got comics written about them. I asked 'what are you tired of seeing?', and by jove they told me.

From those emails Anwar and JD formed. I knew JD would be a fan favourite the second they got their first character sketch, but Anwar has been a sort of fan marmite- people either totally get him, or think he's a self obsessed asshat.

I wrote a year of comics quite happily, following some of the Fifty Shades of Grey plotline, with some side barbs so the characters I'd written could come out and play. Then I reached a lull in the story- a moment where I'd be happy to leave it and move onto a different comic, or continue into a bigger story arc that means I'd be writing what is basically a parody of a crap book for at least another year.

So I asked the internet what they wanted by running another Kickstarter. And to my amazement, the little comic that started out as a joke got enough backers to ensure it's second year and become the book you have in your hands today.

Thank you my beautiful backers, this book is for you.

Kind regards, Tab Artemis Kimpton

Dear Universe.

So, I went to a fetish club last night.

...I know right? Well it turned out to be both what I expected, and the exact opposite at the same time.

Let me start at the beginning.

JD wanted to go. They always tinge their requests so it flatters the shit out of me and I forget what I've agreed to.

Huff *huff*
Yeah?

Hey 'War, you free Friday night?

Prayers finish at 8, then I could head into town—
Why?

choke

Want to go with me to that kinky club evening I told you about?

cough

cough

...what?

I'm going to put this in my 'most bizarre evening of my life' box.

4

It had a 'no t-shirt and jeans' rule so I went in all black.

(But what if I had a fetish for jeans? The *nerve* of these people.)

Chris later explained to me that it's to make people all put some effort into dressing up, so the people who get fancy don't feel out of place.

Oh yeah, Chris.

Then we talked for hours about everything from computing theory to Dr Who (which got many other people joining in).

Hey, sorry to interrupt—

but don't you have work tomorrow?

Shit yeah, I can't check my phone.

What time even is it?

I think I might go back again.

You know, because JD enjoyed it.

14

Dear Universe,

Guess who I served at work today?

None other than a MrRedVixen, though he was less vixen-like and more boring-man-in-his-fourties.

Dear Universe,

Could you stop throwing me into these situations please?

Just once?

Today started with a text from JD...

22

27

He had been joking, I'm sure of it.

The problem is, I have no idea what I would have done if he had been serious.

...Or what I wanted him to do.

Sure I can't give you a lift?

Nah, I'm cool thanks.

It's only a little way to mine.

Fuck, I can't do this again.

A while later...

Come on this has been going on for hourssss.

Just stop already no one cares.

Let her win so we can go drinking.

Because she's a girl?

This is why women don't respect you.

33

And a while after that...

I didn't fall in love straight away, more guiltily slunk into it.

Despite all the shit we went through, JD is still my best friend, and I hope they always will be.

Some days I realise how much I still love them and hate myself a little bit. But some days it's not so bad and I can just enjoy being their friend.

Though some days the line between best friend and what I want in a relationship blur and it feels worse than ever.

Dear Universe,

I didn't get my 2:1.

I bombed my last exam, and just came short.

I Just...

Fuck this.

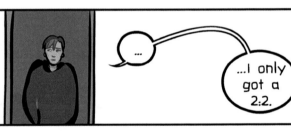

...

...I only got a 2:2.

Oh my little Anakin, you'll become a jedi one day.

I should've just gone into medicine like Uncle Waheed said.

Maybe then I'd be able to get a job.

41

Dear Universe.

So yeah, last night I did a thing.

It was not a smart thing.

45

Turns out I'm a flirty drunk. Still don't want to have sex, but kissing seemed like a fantastic idea.

Another few seconds and I'd have worked up the courage to kiss JD, consequences be dammed.

50

51

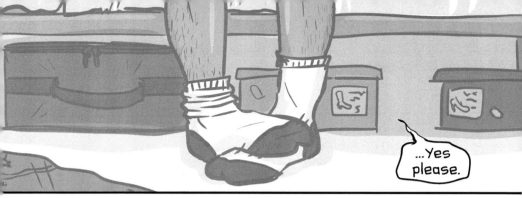

57

OMG I ACTUALLY kissed him. asdfghjkllfkjsdflkjg;lf   #Headdesk

Dear Universe,

I spent most of my time with JD lying through my teeth so they would like me.

I'd been considering JD as 'girlfriend' material as I'd assumed that they were asexual like me.   Personal bias I guess?

But as you may have guessed, JD is really into sex.

Really into it.

I'm not going to let a misunderstanding like that happen again.

And I may fuck up things with Chris, but at least this time I'll be honest about it. I'm going to call him and-

...dammit.

Dear Universe,

Chris called back and said 'we need to talk'. Fuuuu-

I'll put the kettle on— nice cup of tea then a chat.

CHAT!

About what?

We don't need to chat—

—we can watch a movie—

—hey look at all these great movies you have!

If you haven't noticed, I'm not exactly great at being honest and open about my feelings.

Anwar...

Okay fiinnne. Whatever.

We can be *mature* about this.

So...

Sorry I made shit weird. I thought we had a thing but clearly we don't–

–So we can just ignore what I did and go back to being friends.

Turns out Chris is blunt enough for the both of us.

...I think we do have a thing.

Choke

I asked for what I wanted and ACTUALLY GOT IT.

Well, sort of.

Okay, so maybe I was upset; I don't like being reminded what I can't give other people, even if it's completely true.

I've had sex before and it was *alright.*
I enjoy making the other person happy, you know?

The problem is when people want me to like it as much as them, and that's something I can't do.

No matter how much I want to.

Though to be fair, that was then, back before I learned to use my words.

79

I guess if it goes to shit we can just break up and it will be fine.

Right?

Dear Universe,

So you're coming to Jesters with us tonight right?

I...um

Lemmie check...

We had plans tonight right? Please help, avoiding shitty work outing.

86

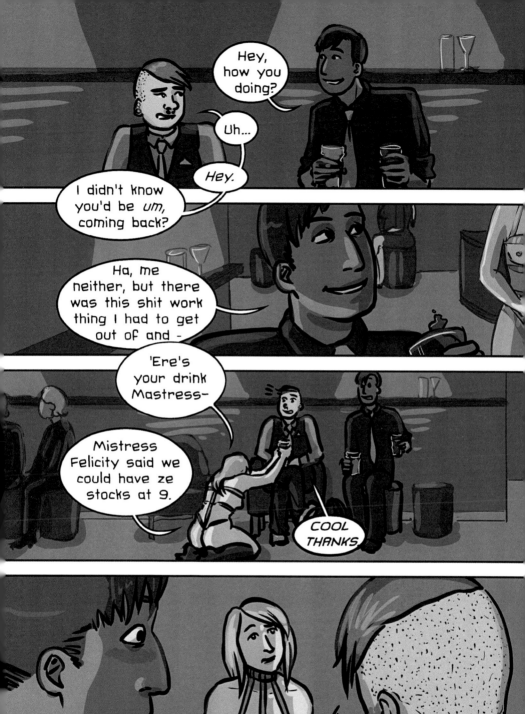

Things are going well with Chris.

We've had a couple of dates, mainly dinner- nothing too fast.

I met Chris' Domme.

I spent the entire time thinking: 'I have to like her—
if I don't like her Chris will dump me'.

91

And 'If she doesn't like me Chris will dump me.'

'Or maybe he won't because if SHE'S the dickhead then he should dump her for being an asshole.'

So instead of being polite I panicked and my mouth took over.

Turns out scary Mistress women talk about the same shit the rest of us do.

Though for all that angst, the awkward small talk was the least of my troubles.

Do you need to leave?

Nah, I'm doing okay.

No, I mean,

don't look,

but JD and their pair are playing in the open dungeon and I'm not sure—

What?

I said don't look!

96

103

105

110

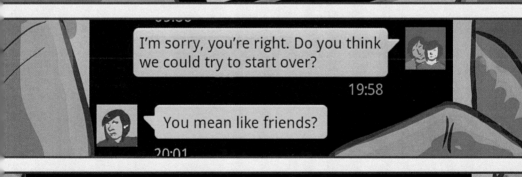
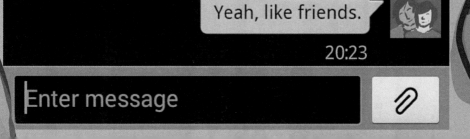

One day I'll get over JD and this will stop hurting so much.

And the stuff with Chris . . .

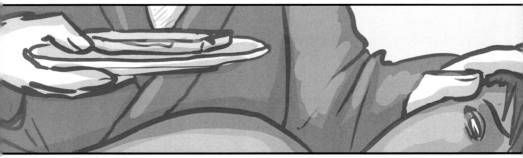

. . . it helps.

I don't want to fuck this up.

Dear Universe,

I should be used to JD being with other people by now.

But none of them were what I felt to be 'true competition'.

Whatever *that* means.

117

118

119

JD and I will never have the same relationship.

But if I'm lucky we might get something even better.

About the author

Tab Kimpton is a full time costume maker and comic writer. He works around the UK attending cons, selling queer comics, witty t-shirts, shiny steampunk goods and giving weird, yet helpful panels.

He's the author of the finished work Khaos Komix, an LGBT* webcomic following the lives of eight teens and their experiences of gender and sexuality.

Read the rest of Shades of A on DiscordComics.com

Check out his other work at KhaosKomix.com and KhaosKostumes.com

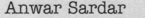

Anwar Sardar   Age: 23

Anwar's parents both came from Pakistan but Anwar grew up in England and doesn't speak Punjabi. His dad was a taxi driver and died when he was 12, leaving him with his mother who trained to become a gynaecologist after his dad's death. His extended family wanted him to go into medicine like her but he decided to get a degree in English Literature and being a giant sass pants instead.

A secret lover of romance movies, Anwar's an asexual with a squishy and previously broken heart, currently protected with a thick layer of sarcasm. The only place he's truly himself is on his blog, where he lets his inane ramblings drift into the universe.

Jaidee Roberts   Age: 22

JD is a voluptuous nerd with a keen eye for thought provoking photography with the first person shooter reflexes of a god. They're a type of genderqueer person who likes to be referred to as 'They' and consider themselves to be more a mix of all genders than an absence of either.

With a mother from Thailand, JD has a taste for really hot food, though they're banned from cooking in their shared house because of the smell of fish oil. JD also has a taste for really hot, experimental sex and will only ever call someone a slut as a term of endearment.

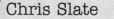

Chris Slate   Age: 37

Chris is an IT technician with a stressful job who takes a break by dressing up pretty and having Mistress Raven do what she wants to him. His two children, Pearl and Hazel live with his ex wife, Susan, but she hates cats so Poof came with him in the move.

A big of a collector of movies, Chris hoards old cheesy sci-fi and horror flicks and laments why he let his parents talk him out of going into directing. Most of his social life is now through the kink community where he trades DIY with Mistress Felicity for helping him learn how to sew.

Claudius 'Poof' Slate   Age: 5

A long haired ginger tom cat with a penchant for food, food and shockingly more food, Poof is a miserable looking kitty who if asked if he's content with life will answer 'Meow.'

He spends his life trolling his owner, playing with super fun electronic cables and sleeping.

Tab reads Fifty Shades of Grey

A Study in Fifty Shades

I can go on and on about how bad Fifty Shades Grey is, but here's some extracts of my annotated copy so you can make the judgement yourself.

too.

"I'm used to getting my own way, Anastasia," he murmurs. "In all things." ~ *well you Shouldn't.*

"I don't doubt it. Why haven't you asked me to call you by your

exposed wire. I gasp involuntarily as I feel it all the way down to somewhere dark and unexplored, deep in my belly. Desperately, I scrabble around for my equilibrium. *Like my colon.*

"He was with me when you phoned.

"In Seattle?" I'm confused.

"No, I'm staying at the Heathman."

Still? Why?

"How did you find me?"

"I tracked your cell phone, Anastasia." *WHUT.*

An extract of the *un-negotiated* Dom/sub contract:

The Submissive will eat regularly well-being from a prescribed list of foods (Appendix 4). The Submissive will not snack between meals, with the exception of fruit.

Clothes:

During the Term, the Submissive will wear clothing only approved by the Dominant. The Dominant will provide a

Mmmm. Hawt.

Glossary of terms

Asexual- Someone who does not experience sexual attraction. This is different to celibacy which is a choice to not engage in sex though the desire is still present. Some asexual people experience romantic attraction and have romantic relationships.

Genderqueer- a person who does not sit in the gender binary and identifies with neither, both, or a combination of male and female. Some genderqueer people use gender neutral pronouns with the singular 'they', 'ze' and 'hir' being the most common. If in doubt, ask!

Transgender- An umbrella term that covers anyone who does not conform to typical gender roles.

Transsexual- Someone who wishes to be considered by society full time as a member of the opposite biological sex.

Transvestite- A person who dresses in clothing traditionally associated with the opposite sex. In the kink community it has associations with sexual gratification, though it can also just mean someone who cross dresses. Now considered a bit of an outdated term, it is a label that can be offensive to some due to the sexual connotations, so should only use it if you're sure it's a term someone identifies with.

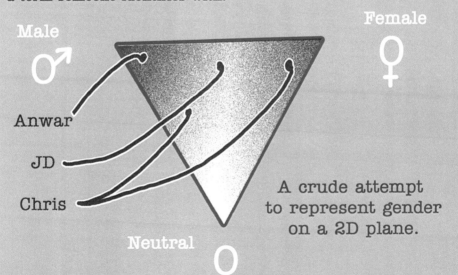

Male

Female

Anwar

JD

Chris

A crude attempt to represent gender on a 2D plane.

Neutral

BDSM- A shortened acronym of Bondage and Discipline, Dominance and Submission, Sadism and Masochism often used as a catch all for anything in the kink scene. Powerplay and the exchange of roles is a common theme of kink relationships, however many fetishists are also welcomed under the BDSM banner.

Kink- Kink sexual practices go beyond what are considered conventional sexual practices as a means of heightening the intimacy between sexual partners. Can be a noun or adjective e.g. Kinksters gather in the kink scene to discuss their kinks. A fetish is similar to a kink, but a fetish is often defined as something a person can't have sex without, whereas a kink is something added for spice.

Consent- Consent plays a massive role in BDSM. Before people begin playing together they set out their limits as part of negotiating what they want out of a scene and often a safeword is agreed upon. A safeword is something any participant in the scene can say if things go too far, and indicates an immediate withdrawl of consent to continue. Anyone that ignores a safeword is a FUCKING douchebag and pretty much committing sexual assault.

Some names for the person
who controls the activity

Top Dominant
Big Owner Master
Sir Madam Mistress
Ma'am Mastress Daddy

Switch

Some names for the person
who is controlled

Bottom Submissive
Little Dog Bitch
Slave Pet Boy Girl

50 Shades of Anwar

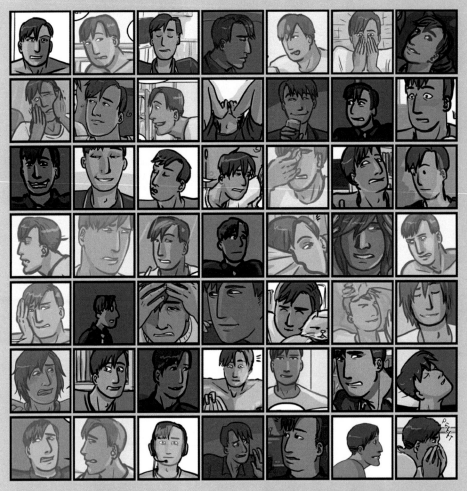